English Revision

Helpful hints for parents

- Start at the beginning of the book and try to work through the activities in order.
- Encourage your child to work independently as much as possible, without referring to the answers!
- Discuss any areas that your child finds particularly tricky and don't worry if he or she finds any of the exercises too difficult. Remember, children learn different things at different rates.
- Give help and lots of praise, rewarding your child by adding stickers to the reward certificate for great work and effort.
- Once you have completed the workbook, move on to the practice pages bound in the centre.

Autumn
Publishing

Nouns, verbs and adjectives

Complete these sentences by adding nouns, verbs or adjectives.

1. I got a ________________ for my birthday.

2. On Saturday, we are ________________ to the ________________.

3. I love ________________.

4. Help! I'm ________________.

5. The ________________ dog ________________ its tail.

remember:

Proper nouns are names of people, places (eg countries, cities, towns, rivers), days and months.

Re-write these sentences so that the proper nouns start with capital letters.

1. mrs jones is taking us swimming on friday.

____

2. ben nevis is the highest mountain in great britain.

____

3. The spanish flag is red and yellow.

____

4. The river seine runs through paris, france.

____

5. roald dahl is my sister annie's favourite author.

____

Write some more nouns, proper nouns, verbs and adjectives here:

Nouns	Proper nouns	Verbs	Adjectives
__________	__________	__________	__________
__________	__________	__________	__________
__________	__________	__________	__________
__________	__________	__________	__________

Complete these collective nouns.

1. a shoal of __________
2. a flock of __________
3. a pack of __________
4. a crowd of __________
5. a pod of __________

WHAT DO A LITTER OF KITTENS AND A GAGGLE OF GEESE HAVE IN COMMON? A ***LITTER*** AND A ***GAGGLE*** ARE COLLECTIVE NOUNS.

Think of a synonym (a similar adjective) for each of the following words.

The first one has been done for you.

1. nice – good, pleasant, polite, okay
2. angry – __________
3. curious – __________

Think of an antonym (an opposite adjective) for each of these words.

1. disappointed – __________
2. excited – __________
3. perfect – __________

Pronouns, adverbs and powerful verbs

Read these sentences and decide which one sounds the most interesting.

WEAK VERB

1. The dog **went** across the road.

BETTER VERB

2. The dog **ran** across the road.

VERB + ADVERB

3. The dog **ran quickly** across the road.

POWERFUL VERB

4. The dog **dashed** across the road.

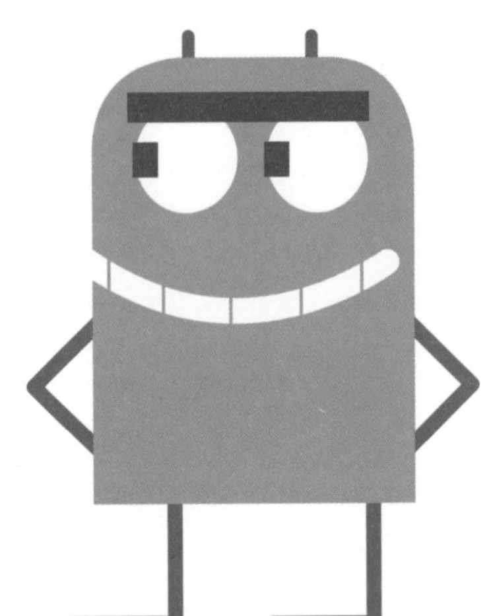

The sentence with the powerful verb is the most interesting. It is better to use one powerful word rather than lots of weaker ones.

Read the following text. Replace the weak verbs and adverbs (underlined) with powerful verbs and adverbs.

Choose from the following:
livid, approaching, dashed, apologised, secured, shouted, escaped

The dog <u>ran</u> across the road. A car was <u>coming</u> and the dog's owner <u>called</u> out to it. Luckily, the dog and the driver <u>didn't have any</u> injury but the driver was <u>very angry</u>. The owner <u>said he was sorry</u> and <u>put</u> the dog on its lead.

Write appropriate adverbs in the spaces below.
The first one has been done for you. Try to use a different adverb each time.

remember:
Adverbs tell us more about verbs. They often end in –ly.

1. The snow fell softly.
2. The dog growled ______________.
3. The ice melted ______________.
4. The leaves ______________ rustled.
5. I walked ______________ down the stairs.
6. My heart was beating ______________.
7. Her hand gripped me ______________.
8. I held on to the reins ______________.

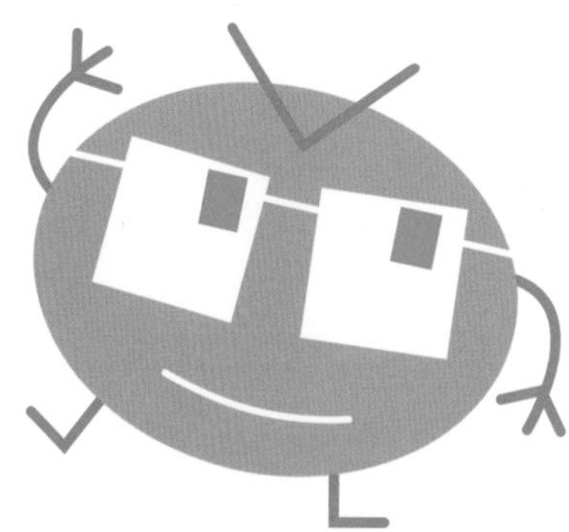

remember:
These words are pronouns: I, he, she, it, we, us, you, they, them.

You can use pronouns to avoid repeating people's names in a text.

Write the missing pronouns in this story.
Then continue it in your own way:

Once upon a time, there was a nosy little girl called Goldie Looks. _________ was walking down the street one day (_________ was late for school, as usual) when _________ saw a house. _________ had a grimy, dusty door. Goldie pushed the door and _________ opened! Inside _________ saw three

____

____

____

Difficult spellings

Learn to spell difficult words by grouping the letters.

remember:

Syllables are groups of sounds that you can hear in words.

For example:

Steg- o- saur- us

There are four syllables in Stegosaurus.

Learn to spell these words by breaking them into syllables:

information ______________________________

understand ______________________________

Saturday ______________________________

February ______________________________

LOOK, SAY, COVER, WRITE, CHECK: LOOK AT THE WORD, SAY IT, COVER IT, WRITE IT, CHECK IT.

Learn to spell difficult words by grouping the letters. Underline the parts of these words that are tricky to remember and learn to spell them.

famous	convenient
earring	solution
photograph	fabulous
pollution	stirring
jealous	immediate
mountain	position

Learn these 'ie' / 'ei' words:

remember:

'i' before 'e' except after 'c', or when it sounds like 'ay'.

field	receive
thief	ceiling
niece	seize
believe	eight
achieve	weight
retrieve	freight
friend	reign

'EI' SOUNDS LIKE 'AY'

THAT'S WEIRD!

There are a couple of exceptions to the rule, eg weird! You will just have to learn to remember them.

remember:

Homonyms are words that sound the same but are spelled differently and have a different meaning.

Homonyms:

pear and pair	break and brake	there and their
right and write	where and wear	fair and fare

Make sure you know the different uses of these homonyms.

Now choose any four homonyms from the list and write a sentence for each.

1. ____________________

2. ____________________

3. ____________________

4. ____________________

1st, 2nd and 3rd person

remember:

First person uses the pronouns: I, me, we, us

Second person uses the pronouns: you, your

Third person uses the pronouns: he, she, it, they

The narrator is the person in the text who tells the story.

Change the pronouns (underlined) in this text from the first to the third person.

I was now beginning to grow handsome; my coat had grown fine and soft, and was bright black. I had one white foot and a pretty white star on my forehead.

Change the pronouns (underlined) in this text from the third person to the first person.

At this time he used to stand in the stable, and his coat was brushed every day till it shone like a rook's wing. It was early in May, when there came a man from Squire Gordon's who took him away to the Hall.

Extracts from 'Black Beauty' by Anna Sewell.

'BLACK BEAUTY' IS WRITTEN IN THE FIRST PERSON: THE HORSE, BLACK BEAUTY, NARRATES THE STORY. STORIES WRITTEN IN THE FIRST PERSON ENCOURAGE THE READER TO EMPATHISE WITH THE MAIN CHARACTER.

Read this job advertisement. It is written in the second person.

IF **YOU** LOVE HORSES THEN THIS IS THE JOB FOR **YOU**!

You can...

- help muck out the stables each day.
- groom and feed the horses.
- have **your** riding lessons for free!

*What are **you** waiting for? **You** can apply now!*

remember:

The pronouns 'you' and 'your' are speaking directly to the reader. Advertisers like to use these pronouns because they are friendly and persuasive.

Now it's your turn to write. Continue the following text:

A diary – in first person

Today ____

____

An instruction – in second person

This is what you do: ____

____

A description – in third person

She/he looked like ____

____

____

____

Powerful prefixes and suffixes

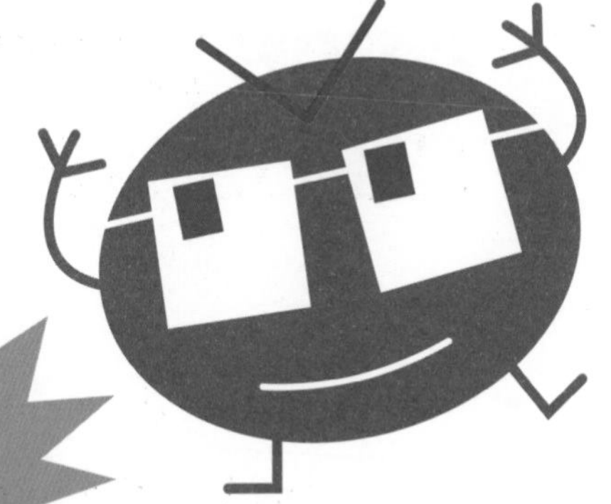

remember:

A **prefix** is a group of letters at the beginning of a word.
A **suffix** is a group of letters at the end of a word.

These prefixes and suffixes can change the meaning of the root word to its exact opposite.

For example:

truth**ful**	thought**ful**	cloud**y**
untrue	thought**less**	cloud**less**

Write one word from each pair (above) in these sentences.

1. It was a grey and ____________________ day.

2. She behaved in a cruel and ____________________ way.

3. The thief lied. His statement was ____________________ .

Choose from the remaining words to complete these sentences.

1. It was a bright and ____________________ day.

2. She behaved in a kind and ____________________ way.

3. The thief did not lie. His statement was ____________________ .

Add the prefix dis- to change these words.

agree	honest	interested
disagree ________	________	________
like	obedient	advantage
________	________	________
appear	continued	loyal
________	________	________

Write three sentences using any of the dis- words above. You can change the tense (with a different suffix) if you prefer.

1. ____________________

2. ____________________

3. ____________________

Change these words to mean more than one.

baby ________ wolf ________

memory ________ knife ________

discovery ________ child ________

fox ________ sheep ________

cactus ________ volcano ________

fungus ________ tomato ________

remember:

Suffixes can change words from singular to plural.

THERE ARE A COUPLE OF WORDS SET TO TEST YOU IN THIS LIST!

Conjunctions

remember:

A **conjunction** is a connecting word (sometimes called a connective) that links clauses or sentences.

For example:

Kim loves sport. She hates swimming.

Kim loves sport **but** she hates swimming.

Conjunctions:

and	so	or	when
but	if	because	while

Use a conjunction to join two sentences into one sentence:

1. Dan and Kim are friends. They are always arguing.

____

2. Kim usually wins. She shouts the loudest!

____

3. Kim came home late last night. She's still asleep.

____

4. Dan gets worried. Kim gets home late.

____

Connecting adverbs

remember:
Sometimes we use adverbs to connect sentences and paragraphs so that our writing 'flows' better.

Connecting adverbs:

after	now	later	finally	however
then	next	suddenly	firstly	consequently

Put these sentences in the correct order.

Look for the connecting words to help you. Number the sentences from 1 to 8.

☐ Next, their tails become shorter.
[1] Frogs lay their eggs, called 'frog spawn', in water.
☐ After a few weeks tiny tadpoles hatch.
☐ First they grow their back legs.
☐ The tiny tadpoles breathe through gills, like fish.
☐ Then they grow their front legs at about ten weeks old.
☐ Finally, they can jump out of the water and breathe air!
☐ Now they look like tiny frogs.

TOP TIP FOR BUDDING AUTHORS: A FAMOUS AUTHOR ONCE SAID, "IT'S EASY; ALL YOU HAVE TO DO IS PUT THE RIGHT WORDS IN THE RIGHT ORDER."

Now write out the sentences in the correct order below.

____

____

____

____

____

____

____

____

Clauses

remember:

A **clause** can be a whole sentence or part of a sentence.

A **simple** sentence has one clause.

A **complex** sentence has two or more clauses.

A **main** clause could be a sentence by itself.

A **subordinate** clause would not make sense by itself.

For example: Kim snores when she is sleeping.

Kim snores is the main clause.

when she is sleeping is the subordinate clause.

Join each main clause to a subordinate clause to make one sentence with two clauses.

Main clause	**Subordinate clause**
1. Many mammals are intelligent	to hide from their enemies.
2. Baby mammals feed on their mother's milk	when they are born.
3. Some mammals have camouflage markings	and can learn to do new things.

Underline the main clause in each sentence below.

1. Mammals' bodies stay the same temperature whether it is hot or cold.

2. Some mammals grow a thicker coat in the winter months.

3. Some mammals like to live in groups when they are in the wild.

MORE TENSES

Underline the verbs in the sentences below and rewrite the sentences in the past tense.

1. He puts the box on the table with a thud.

    ____

2. The dog barks as Mark throws a treat.

    ____

3. Zoey searches every room for her tennis racket.

    ____

4. Mrs Piper buys three bunches of flowers for the house.

    ____

5. Rob finds his crayons and begins drawing.

    ____

6. Gracie starts to read her book but it gets scary so she puts it down.

    ____

7. Kim solves the mystery of the missing trophy and gives it back to its rightful owner.

    ____

8. The fire alarm goes off and everyone runs out of the school.

    ____

9. Evie listens to her favourite music while she completes her homework.

    ____

10. The bird sings from the treetop and wakes the cat.

    ____

Answers: 1. He put the box on the table with a thud. 2. The dog barked as Mark threw a treat. 3. Zoey searched every room for her tennis racket. 4. Mrs Piper bought three bunches of flowers for the house. 5. Rob found his crayons and began drawing. 6. Gracie started to read her book but it got scary so she put it down. 7. Kim solved the mystery of the missing trophy and gave it back to its rightful owner. 8. The fire alarm went off and everyone ran out of the school. 9. Evie listened to her favourite music while she completed her homework. 10. The bird sang from the treetop and woke the cat.

REVISE YOUR SPELLINGS

Read the word pairs. Tick the words that are spelled correctly.

always or allways
animul or animal
anuther or another
around or arownd
balloon or baloon
befor or before
being or bein
birthday or burthday
bruther or brother
can't or cant
chaing or change
children or childrun
comeing or coming
didn't or didnt
diffrent or different
does or dus
don't or dont
evry or every

havf *or* half
head *or* hed
heard *or* hurd
I'm *or* Im
important *or* importent
jumped *or* jumpt
leave *or* leeve
light *or* lyte
money *or* munny
muther *or* mother
never *or* nevver
numbr *or* number
only *or* onely
uther *or* other
outside *or* owtside
paper *or* papeer
question *or* qestion
rownd *or* round

Answers: always, animal, another, around, balloon, before, being, birthday, brother, can't, change, children, coming, didn't, different, does, don't, every, half, head, heard, I'm, important, jumped, leave, light, money, mother, never, number, only, other, outside, paper, question, round

PUNCTUATION TEST

Add the missing punctuation to the following story text:

Will you call him killer, like your auntys old cat she asked

No he is much more handsome than old killer ever was

Yes he really is quite a cutie, and he has such a sweet-tempered face and a softness around the eyes – why dont you call him kitty

You will need:

3 pairs of speech marks ☐ ☐ ☐

2 question marks ☐ ☐

2 full stops ☐ ☐

2 commas ☐ ☐

3 capital letters ☐ ☐ ☐

2 apostrophes ☐ ☐

Tick the boxes ☐ *as you find the missing punctuation.*

Tick the sentences that use an apostrophe correctly and cross those that don't.

1. That is Tims' bike. ☐
2. The job's are all the same. ☐
3. "I do'nt know where she is." ☐
4. "Shes my best friend." ☐
5. "What's happening here?" ☐
6. The biscuit's were all over the floor. ☐
7. "Aren't you feeling well?" ☐
8. "Its' not fair, I want to!" ☐
9. "Theyl'l be in the car if you havent got them here." ☐
10. The car's tyres are fully inflated. ☐

Answers: "Will you call him Killer, like your aunty's old cat?" she asked.
"No, he is much more handsome than old Killer ever was."
"Yes, he really is quite a cutie, and he has such a sweet-tempered face and a softness around the eyes – why don't you call him Kitty?"

1. X 2. X 3. X 4. X 5. ✓ 6. X 7. ✓ 8. X 9. X 10. ✓

TESTING TIMES

1. Where could you add a **semicolon** in this text?

   She opened the cage door slowly in the darkness she could just make out the outline of an animal.

2. Underline the **pronouns** in this text. Is it written in first, second or third person?

   Text this number for your chance to win this week's bonus prize – a holiday for two in a resort of your choice!

3. Underline the word that **connects** these two sentences.

   The detective suspected this was a lie. However, he didn't cross-examine the suspect at this point.

4. Write the missing **colon** in this text.

   You need to decide between these colours red, yellow, blue or green.

5. Write a list of your favourite things here, adding **commas** and/or **semicolons** to separate each item in the list. Write 'and' before the last item and end with a full stop.

   My favourite things are: ______________________________

   ____

6. Replace the verb (underlined) with a more **powerful verb**.

   Dinosaurs walked the Earth 65 million years ago.

7. Write a phrase containing a **possessive apostrophe** for each of the following:

   the dog belonging to the family ______________________________

   the sweets belonging to Jack ______________________________

   the books belonging to the girls ______________________________

   the ball belonging to the players ______________________________

1. She opened the cage door slowly; in the darkness she could just make out the outline of an animal. 2. It is written in the second person. Text this number for your chance to win this week's bonus prize – a holiday for two in a resort of your choice! 3. However 4. You need to decide between these colours: red, yellow, blue or green. 5. You can mark this one yourself! 7. the family's dog, Jack's sweets, the girls' books, the players' ball

Active and passive verbs

For example:

The dog <u>chased</u> the cat. —— ACTIVE

The cat <u>was chased by</u> the dog. —— PASSIVE

The active sentence is about what the dog did.

The passive sentence is about what happened to the cat.

remember:

Some verbs can be **active** or **passive.**

Draw a line from the active to the passive text.

1. The dog picked up the scent.	The cake was made by Molly.
2. Tom read the poem.	The baby was carried by the mother.
3. The mother carried the baby.	The scent was picked up by the dog.
4. Molly made the cake.	The poem was read by Tom.

Write these sentences as passive text.

1. The snake ate the mouse.

___

2. Harry won the prize.

___

3. Some insects drink pollen.

___

4. Plants and animals need oxygen.

___

5. The girl wrote the scary story.

___

Terrible tenses

remember:

Verbs change tense depending on when the action takes place.

For example:

To fly

Past: I flew

Present: I fly

Present (third person): He/she flies

Present continuous: I am flying

Future: I will fly

To swim

Past: I swam

Present: I swim

Present (third person): He/she swims

Present continuous: I am swimming

Future: I will swim

Write the verbs in the correct tense.

To think

Past: I ______________________

Present: I ______________________

Present (third person): He/she ______________________

Present continuous: I am ______________________

Future: I will ______________________

To write

Past: I ______________________

Present: I ______________________

Present (third person): He/she ______________________

Present continuous: I am ______________________

Future: I will ______________________

To eat

Past: I ______________________

Present: I ______________________

Present (third person): He/she ______________________

Present continuous: I am ______________________

Future: I will ______________________

To make

Past: I ______________________

Present: I ______________________

Present (third person): He/she ______________________

Present continuous: I am ______________________

Future: I will ______________________

Borrowed words

Some words we use are borrowed from other languages – this sometimes makes them more difficult to spell!

Words derived from French:	Words derived from Greek:	Words derived from Latin:
café	dinosaur	decimal
restaurant	aqua	adventure
hotel	alpha	century
beauty	amphibian	vice versa
garage	geography	example (eg)
village	biology	etcetera (etc)

remember:

Many scientific words come from Latin or Greek.

OTHER EXAMPLES ARE: ANNO DOMINI (AD), ANTE MERIDIEM (AM)! THAT'S WHY WE LIKE TO ABBREVIATE THEM!

Write some sentences using any of the borrowed words above – or any other borrowed words you know.

1. ______________________________

2. ______________________________

3. ______________________________

4. ______________________________

Similes and metaphors

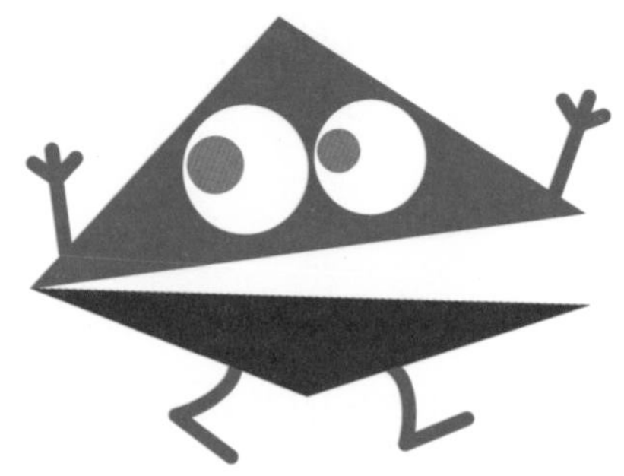

remember:

Similes are when you describe something as being <u>like</u> or <u>as</u> something else.

Similes:

The moon shone **like** a torch.

He felt as strong **as** an ox.

Make up some of your own similes to complete these descriptions.

1. Some dinosaurs were as tall as ____________________
2. The longest dinosaurs were as long as ____________________
3. The smallest dinosaurs were like ____________________
4. Some dinosaurs had teeth like ____________________

remember:

Metaphors are when you say that something <u>is</u> something else. For example, when you say someone **is** a dinosaur – that's a metaphor. It means the person is old-fashioned!

Write your own metaphors to complete these descriptions.

1. She is a ____________________ in the swimming pool.
2. She is a ____________________ on the race track.
3. He is a ____________________ in the boxing ring.
4. He is a ____________________ on the skateboard.

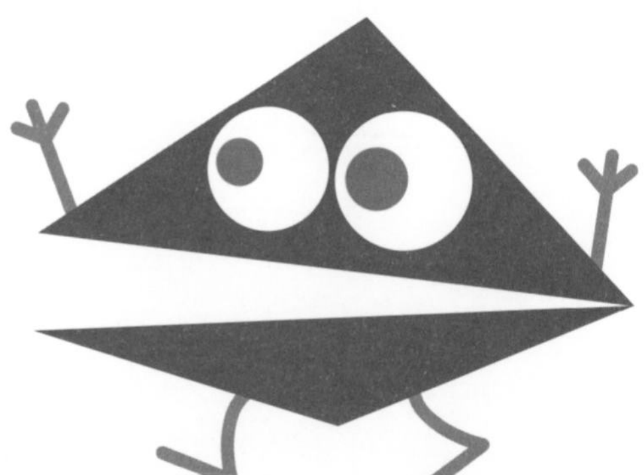

Personification

Personification:

The sun smiled.

The grey sky wept.

The waves roared.

The spooky house groaned.

remember:

Personification is when a writer gives human characteristics to a non-human thing. It is similar to a metaphor.

Make up some of your own personifications to complete these descriptions. You can add an adjective before the noun if you want to.

1. The road ______________________________
2. The ships ______________________________
3. The car ______________________________
4. The computer ______________________________

POP!

BUZZ!

CRASH!

SQUELCH!

SQUEAK!

GLUG!

PLOP!

remember:

Onomatopoeia is a word that sounds like the thing it is describing.

Complete each sentence below using an onomatopoeic word. The first one has been done for you.

1. The water sloshed on the floor.
2. The door ______________________________
3. The gate ______________________________
4. The plate ______________________________

Proverbs and idioms

remember:
Proverbs are common sayings or comments about life.

Write what you think these proverbs mean.

1. Birds of a feather flock together.

____

2. The early bird catches the worm.

____

3. Put your best foot forward.

____

4. Don't cry over spilt milk.

____

5. It never rains but it pours.

____

Write what you think these idioms mean.

remember:
Idioms are not meant to be taken literally. Don't use idioms in formal (serious) writing.

over the moon ______________________________

under the weather ______________________________

in the same boat ______________________________

touch and go ______________________________

high and mighty ______________________________

home and dry ______________________________

Standard English

remember:
You should use standard English in your writing at school – except perhaps in story writing when you want to make a character's direct speech sound more realistic.

Write these sentences using standard (formal) English.

1. I won you in that race.

____

2. It was him what done it.

____

3. Let me lend your book.

____

4. I'm the bestest.

____

5. Me and my sister was lost.

____

6. We was scared.

____

7. Thems my shoes.

____

8. Here's the lunch what I bought.

____

Limericks and poems

Use different colours to circle the words that rhyme.

There was an old man from Peru
Who dreamed he was eating his shoe.
He woke in a fright
In the middle of the night
And found it was perfectly true!
Anon

There was an old man with a beard,
Who said, "It is just as I feared –
Two owls and a hen,
Four larks and a wren
Have all built their nests in my beard!"
Edward Lear

Make up a limerick about a pet, someone you know or yourself.

Base it on the examples above.

remember:

A limerick is a humorous verse of five lines, with the rhyming pattern: a, a, b, b, a.

Poetry can make us laugh, make us cry, or make us think.

Read this classic poem.

Hurt no living thing.
Ladybird, nor butterfly,
Nor moth with dusty wing,
Nor cricket chirping cheerily,
Nor grasshopper so light of leap,
Nor dancing gnat, nor beetle fat,
Nor harmless worms that creep.

Christina Rossetti

Write a poem in the style of 'Hurt no living thing'.
Choose your own animals and rhyming words.
Try to follow a similar rhyming pattern.

____

____

____

____

____

____

____

____

____

____

I KNOW THE SHORTEST POEM IN THE ENGLISH LANGUAGE. IT'S CALLED 'FLEAS'.
Fleas
Adam 'ad 'em.

Punctuation

Punctuation helps the reader understand what is written.
Writing is clearer when we write in sentences using full stops, capital letters, commas, semicolons, question marks, exclamation marks, speech marks, etc.

remember:

- A full stop (.) goes at the end of a sentence where we would pause.
- A comma (,) separates ideas within a sentence and items in a list.
- A semicolon (;) joins sentences or phrases that are closely connected.
- A colon (:) starts a list or a new idea.
- An apostrophe (’) shows you who owns something.
  It also shows you where words have been shortened.
- A question mark (?) tells you that a question is being asked.
- An exclamation mark (!) shows surprise, humour or excitement.
- Speech marks (“ ”) tell you exactly what words are spoken.

A COMMA (,) IS A SHORT PAUSE, A SEMICOLON (;) IS SLIGHTLY LONGER AND A FULL STOP (.) IS THE LONGEST PAUSE.

Add the missing punctuation to this story extract.

Will you read me a spooky story Tim asked

Only if you promise to go to sleep afterwards Tims dad replied

Yes I promise said Tim

His dad began to read It was almost midnight the light of the full moon brushed the trees…

Just when they got to the scariest part of the story all the lights went out

Then they heard a scary laugh Woah ah ah It was Mina Tims big sister playing a trick on them

Dad said Tim later I cant sleep Im too scared Can you read me something happy instead

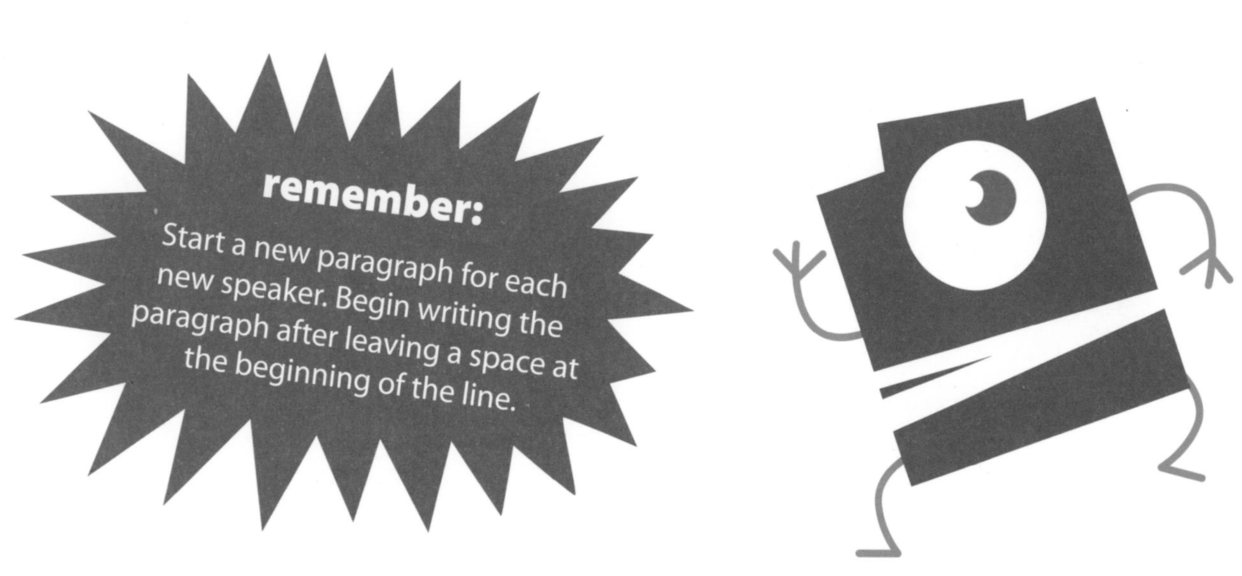

remember:
Start a new paragraph for each new speaker. Begin writing the paragraph after leaving a space at the beginning of the line.

Scary punctuation

Add the missing punctuation to these sentences.

1. The spell included the hair of a dog wings of a bat and a spiders web
2. Suddenly the door slammed shut
3. Its very dark in here she whispered
4. I think were trapped cried Sam
5. Its a spell that I cant break she said

Use an apostrophe to shorten words in each of the sentences below.
The first one has been done for you.

6. I have written a ghost story. I've written a ghost story.
7. It is so scary! ______________________
8. You will have to read it. ______________________
9. What is it called? ______________________
10. The witch could not do any magic! ______________________

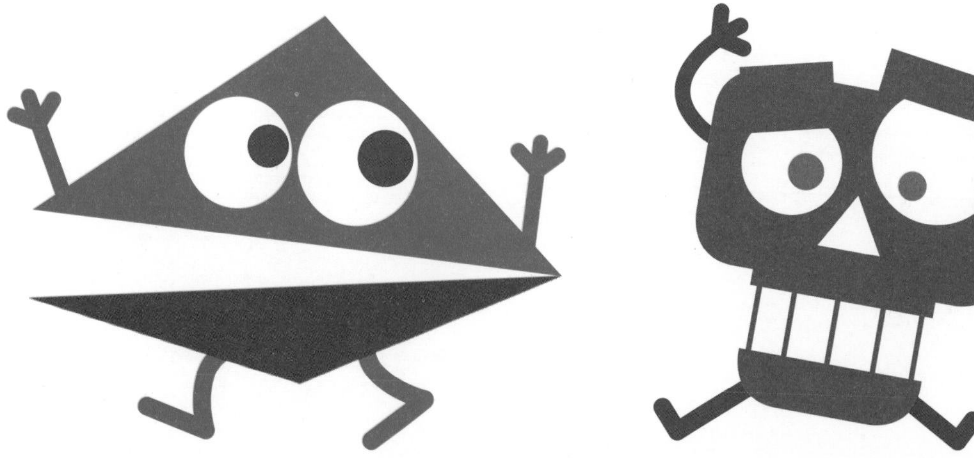

Answers

Nouns, verbs and adjectives

1. Mrs Jones is taking us swimming on Friday.
2. Ben Nevis is the highest mountain in Great Britain.
3. The Spanish flag is red and yellow.
4. The River Seine runs through Paris, France.
5. Roald Dahl is my sister Annie's favourite author.

Here are some possible answers:

1. a shoal of fish
2. a flock of sheep
3. a pack of wolves
4. a crowd of people
5. a pod of dolphins

Here are some possible answers:

1. nice – good, pleasant, polite, okay
2. angry – cross, annoyed, livid
3. curious – interested, inquisitive, questioning

1. disappointed – pleased
2. excited – bored
3. perfect – imperfect

Pronouns, adverbs and powerful verbs

The dog dashed across the road. A car was approaching and the dog's owner shouted out to it. Luckily, the dog and the driver escaped injury but the driver was livid. The owner apologised and secured the dog on its lead.

Once upon a time, there was a nosy little girl called Goldie Looks. She was walking down the street one day (she was late for school, as usual) when she saw a house. It had a grimy, dusty door. Goldie pushed the door and it opened! Inside she saw three …. (to be continued by you!)

Difficult spellings

in-form-a-tion
un-der-stand
Sat-ur-day
Feb-ru-a-ry

1st, 2nd and 3rd person

<u>He</u> was now beginning to grow handsome; <u>his</u> coat had grown fine and soft, and was bright black. <u>He</u> had one white foot and a pretty white star on <u>his</u> forehead.

At this time <u>I</u> used to stand in the stable, and <u>my</u> coat was brushed every day till it shone like a rook's wing. It was early in May, when there came a man from Squire Gordon's who took <u>me</u> away to the Hall.

Powerful prefixes and suffixes

1. It was a grey and cloudy day.
2. She behaved in a cruel and thoughtless way.
3. The thief lied. His statement was untrue.

1. It was a bright and cloudless day.
2. She behaved in a kind and thoughtful way.
3. The thief did not lie. His statement was truthful.

disagree
dislike
disappear
dishonest
disobedient
discontinued
disinterested
disadvantage
disloyal

babies	wolves
memories	knives
discoveries	children
foxes	sheep
cacti	volcanoes
fungi	tomatoes

Conjunctions

Here are some possible answers:

1. Dan and Kim are friends <u>but</u> they are always arguing.
2. Kim usually wins <u>because</u> she shouts the loudest!
3. Kim came home late last night <u>so</u> she's still asleep.
4. Dan gets worried <u>when</u> Kim gets home late.

Connecting adverbs

1 Frogs lay their eggs, called 'frog spawn', in water.
2 After a few weeks tiny tadpoles hatch.
3 The tiny tadpoles breathe through gills, like fish.
4 First they grow their back legs.
5 Then they grow their front legs at about ten weeks old.
6 Next, their tails become shorter.
7 Now they look like tiny frogs.
8 Finally, they can jump out of the water and breathe air!

Clauses

1. Many mammals are intelligent and can learn to do new things.
2. Baby mammals feed on their mother's milk when they are born.
3. Some mammals have camouflage markings to hide from their enemies.

1. <u>Mammals' bodies stay the same temperature</u> whether it is hot or cold.
2. <u>Some mammals grow a thicker coat</u> in the winter months.
3. <u>Some mammals like to live in groups</u> when they are in the wild.

Active and passive verbs

1. The dog picked up the scent. — The scent was picked up by the dog.
2. Tom read the poem. — The poem was read by Tom.
3. The mother carried the baby. — The baby was carried by the mother.
4. Molly made the cake. — The cake was made by Molly.

1. The mouse was eaten by the snake.
2. The prize was won by Harry.
3. Pollen is drunk by some insects.
4. Oxygen is needed by plants and animals.
5. The scary story was written by the girl.

Terrible tenses

I thought	I wrote
I think	I write
He/she thinks	He/she writes
I am thinking	I am writing
I will think	I will write

I ate	I made
I eat	I make
He/she eats	He/she makes
I am eating	I am making
I will eat	I will make

Personification

Here are some possible answers:

1. The water sloshed on the floor.
2. The door slammed shut.
3. The gate creaked open.
4. The plate smashed.

Proverbs and idioms

1. People who share the same interests like to be together.
2. If you need to do something, do it straightaway.
3. Try your best.
4. Don't worry about things you can't change.
5. When bad things happen they come all at once.

over the moon – feeling very happy
under the weather – feeling unwell
in the same boat – in the same situation
touch and go – risky
high and mighty – behaving as if important
home and dry – safe

Standard English

1. I beat you in that race.
2. He did it.
3. Let me borrow your book.
4. I'm the best.
5. My sister and I were lost.
6. We were scared.
7. They are my shoes.
8. Here's the lunch that I bought.

Punctuation

"Will you read me a spooky story?" Tim asked.

"Only if you promise to go to sleep afterwards," Tim's dad replied.

"Yes, I promise," said Tim.

His dad began to read. "It was almost midnight; the light of the full moon brushed the trees…"

Just when they got to the scariest part of the story, all the lights went out!

Then they heard a scary laugh, "Woah-ah-ah!" It was Mina, Tim's big sister, playing a trick on them.

"Dad," said Tim later. "I can't sleep. I'm too scared. Can you read me something happy instead?"

Scary punctuation

1. The spell included: the hair of a dog, wings of a bat and a spider's web.
2. Suddenly the door slammed shut!
3. "It's very dark in here," she whispered.
4. "I think we're trapped!" cried Sam.
5. "It's a spell that I can't break!" she said.
6. I've written a ghost story.
7. It's so scary!
8. You'll have to read it.
9. What's it called?
10. The witch couldn't do any magic!

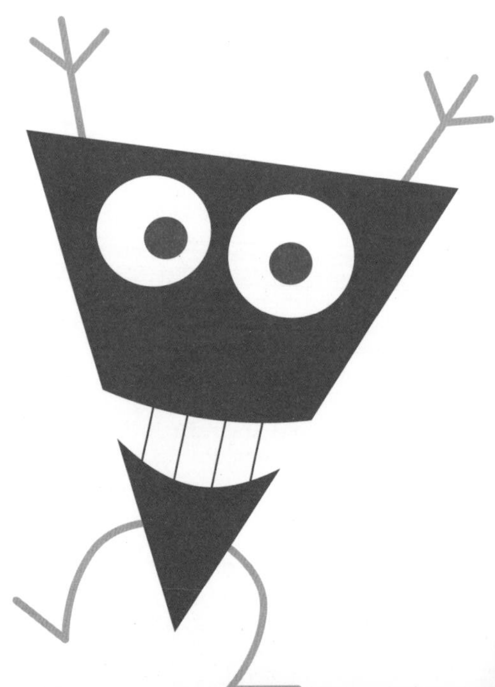